ONCE UPON A
STEM

Rapunzel

Written by **Robin**  ated by **Amy Li**

BookLife
PUBLISHING

©2021
BookLife Publishing Ltd.
King's Lynn
Norfolk PE30 4LS

ISBN: 978-1-83927-170-0

Written by:
Robin Twiddy

Edited by:
Emilie Dufresne

Designed by:
Amy Li

A catalogue record for this book is available from the British Library.

All facts, statistics, web addresses and URLs in this book were verified as valid and accurate at time of writing. No responsibility for any changes to external websites or references can be accepted by either the author or publisher.

Words that look like <u>this</u> can be found in the glossary on page 24.

Photo credits

All images are courtesy of Shutterstock.com, unless otherwise specified. With thanks to Getty Images, Thinkstock Photo and iStockphoto. Recurring images (cover and internal) – artcreator (Professor), Yama-bika, The_Pixel, MoonRock (paper textures), kotoffei, Venomous Vector, illustrator096 (decorative vectors), okawa somchai (leaf texture), P2–3 – Pretty Vectors, Tori20, p4–5 – cluckva, RODINA OLENA, p8–9 – cluckva, Adelyne Tu-manskaya, wkl003mike, p16–17 – bsd, p18–19 – arigato, p20–21 – cluckva, Alex Landa, p22–23 – arigato, Pretty Vectors, Tori20.

Welcome, I am Professor Everafter and I really like STEM subjects. These are science, technology, engineering and mathematics.

Rapunzel

I have been studying fairy tales. This one is called Rapunzel. Some of this story is just silly. I have been trying to see if STEM can help me make sense of it.

Once upon a STEM...

... in a kingdom far, far away, there lived a married couple. Their little house was next to a large walled garden. Nobody ever went into the garden because it was owned by a wicked <u>enchantress</u>.

The wife saw a plant known as rapunzel in the garden. "I must eat that plant. If I don't, I think I might die," she said to her husband. The husband loved his wife dearly, so he crept into the garden that night.

Rapunzel plant

The husband pulled one of the plants from the ground. When he looked up, he froze in fear. Right there in front of him stood the enchantress. She was very angry at the man.

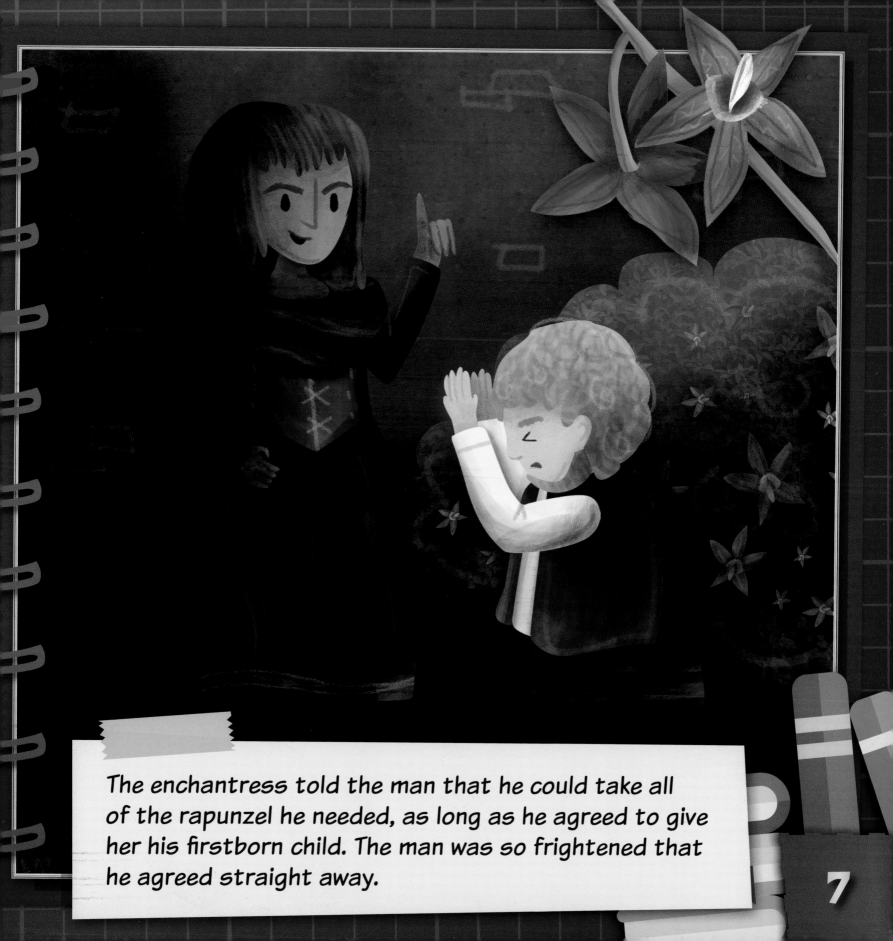

The enchantress told the man that he could take all of the rapunzel he needed, as long as he agreed to give her his firstborn child. The man was so frightened that he agreed straight away.

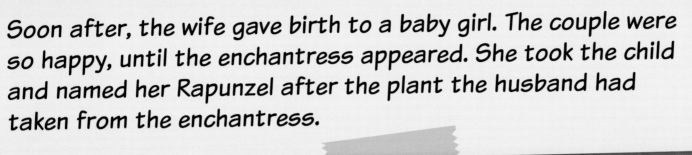

Soon after, the wife gave birth to a baby girl. The couple were so happy, until the enchantress appeared. She took the child and named her Rapunzel after the plant the husband had taken from the enchantress.

8

How many deep, dark woods are there in the land of fairy tales?

The deep, dark wood

The enchantress took Rapunzel to a tall tower in a deep, dark wood. The tower had no stairs or doors, only a window at the very top. Rapunzel grew up all alone in the tower, with only the enchantress for company.

That is a very impressive tower. Very tall. However, even a tower won't keep you safe if there is an earthquake. If the enchantress is clever, she will use her engineering skills here.

If the enchantress added springs to the tower's foundations, they would absorb the movements made by an earthquake. This would mean the ground would move but the tower wouldn't.

This is how springs would control the tower's shaking if there was an earthquake.

Thanks, springs!

1

Rapunzel's hair is easily strong enough for the enchantress to climb it without it breaking. But what about Rapunzel herself? Without an anchor, the weight of the enchantress would either pull the hair straight out of Rapunzel's head or pull her right out of the window.

Together, all the hairs on a person's head are strong enough to support two African elephants.

So, how can we stop Rapunzel getting pulled out of the window when the enchantress is climbing up? Eureka, a hook! If Rapunzel wraps her hair around a strong hook, that will take the weight of the enchantress.

Thank you, Professor!

This means that Rapunzel won't get hurt.

Years later, a prince was walking in the forest when he heard Rapunzel singing. He thought it was beautiful. The prince followed the song to the tower. But no matter how much he searched, he couldn't find a door or way in.

Each day, the prince would come to the tower and listen to Rapunzel sing. One day, he was hidden by the shadow of a tree when he saw the enchantress call up to the window.

The next day the prince returned to the tower and called up to the window, "Rapunzel, Rapunzel, let down your hair!"

The prince climbed up into the window. Only when he was inside did Rapunzel realise that he was not the enchantress.

16

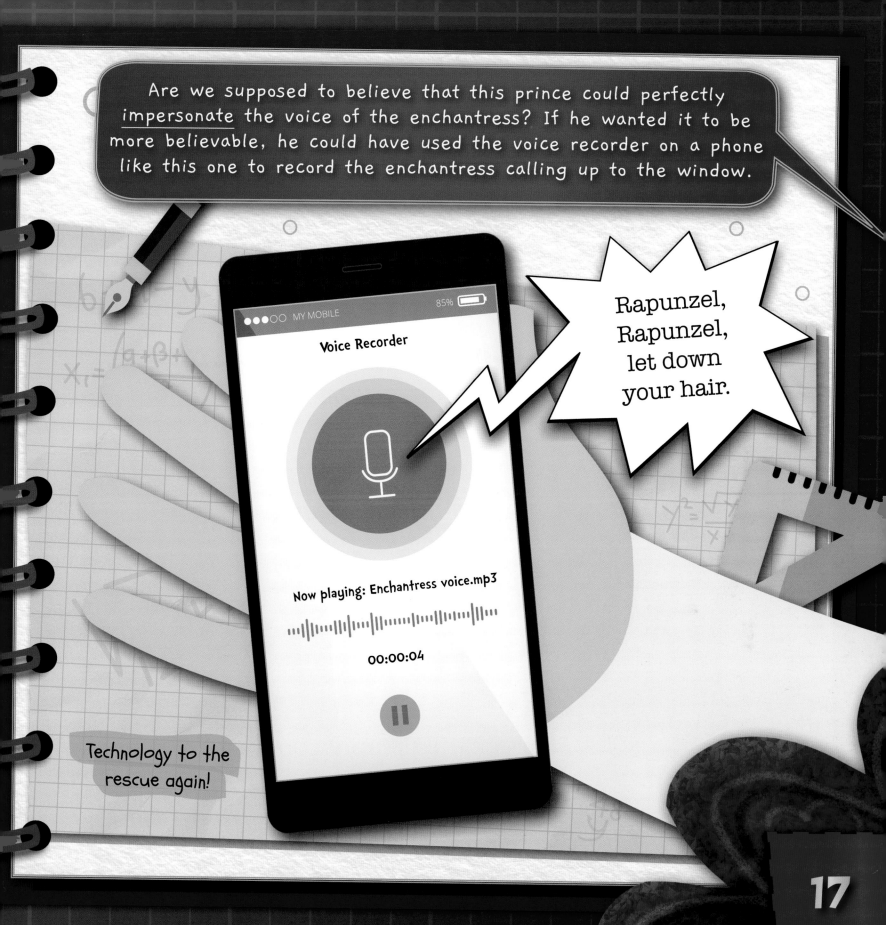

Rapunzel was frightened at first. She had never seen a man before. But soon the two fell in love. The prince asked Rapunzel to run away and marry him. But there was one problem. The only way in or out was to climb Rapunzel's hair.

One day, when the enchantress had climbed up into the window, Rapunzel, without thinking, said, "You are heavier than the prince." The enchantress realised that Rapunzel had been seeing a visitor.

She became so mad that she cut off Rapunzel's lovely hair then sent her to the <u>desert</u> using magic.

It is time to use some maths. Let's find out how much heavier the enchantress was than the prince. If we know the weight of the prince and the enchantress, we should be able to work it out.

Hmmm, the enchantress weighs about **82 kilograms**. And the prince weighs about **63 kilograms**.

82 kilograms – 63 kilograms = 19 kilograms

So, the enchantress weighs 19 kilograms more than the prince.

The enchantress tied Rapunzel's hair to a heavy wardrobe. When the prince climbed into the window later that day, he was horrified to see the enchantress there and fell from the window.

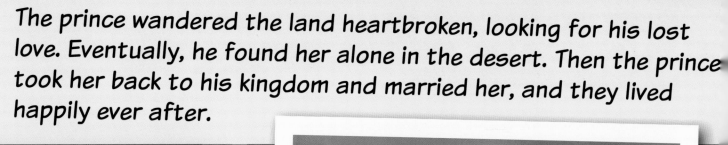

The prince wandered the land heartbroken, looking for his lost love. Eventually, he found her alone in the desert. Then the prince took her back to his kingdom and married her, and they lived happily ever after.

Well, that was a strange story. But with a few tweaks and a little help from STEM, we could save Rapunzel and the prince a lot of time and a lot of heartbreak!

Glossary

absorb	to take in or soak up
anchor	something that holds things in place or weighs them down
desert	a place that gets very little rain and where very few plants and animals can survive
earthquake	vibrations that shake the ground and can damage or knock down buildings
enchantress	a female character in fairy tales who can perform magic
foundations	the bottom parts of buildings that are often dug into the ground to keep a building stable
impersonate	to pretend to be someone else
skein of silk	a piece of silk woven into a rope-like shape
weave	to criss-cross a material, making it stronger

Index